Mystery Mob
and the
Man-eating Tiger

Roger Hurn

Illustrated by
Stik

RISING ★ STARS

Rising Stars UK Ltd.
7 Hatchers Mews, Bermondsey Street, London SE1 3GS
www.risingstars-uk.com

Published 2008
Reprinted 2011, 2012, 2013

Cover design: Burville-Riley Partnership
Illustrator: Stik, Bill Greenhead for Illustration Ltd
Text design and typesetting: Andy Wilson
Publisher: Gill Budgell
Editor: Catherine Baker

British Library Cataloguing in Publication Data.
A CIP record for this book is available from the British Library

ISBN: 978-1-84680-434-2

Printed in the UK by Ashford Colour Press Ltd.

Contents

Meet the Mystery Mob

Name:

Gummy

FYI: Gummy hasn't got much brain – and even fewer teeth.

Loves: Soup.

Hates: Toffee chews.

Fact: The brightest thing about him is his shirt.

Name:

Lee

FYI: If Lee was any cooler he'd be a cucumber.

Loves: Hip-hop.

Hates: Hopscotch.

Fact: He has his own designer label (which he peeled off a tin).

Name:

FYI: Rob lives in his own world – he's just visiting planet Earth.

Loves: Daydreaming.

Hates: Nightmares.

Fact: Rob always does his homework – he just forgets to write it down.

Name:

Dwayne

FYI: Dwayne is smarter than a tree full of owls.

Loves: Anything complicated.

Hates: Join-the-dots books.

Fact: If he was any brighter you could use him as a floodlight at football matches.

Name:

Chet

FYI: Chet is as brave as a lion with steel jaws.

Loves: Having adventures.

Hates: Knitting.

Fact: He's as tough as the chicken his granny cooks for his tea.

Name:

Adi

FYI: Adi is as happy as a football fan with tickets to the big match.

Loves: Telling jokes.

Hates: Moaning minnies.

Fact: He knows more jokes than a jumbo joke book.

1

Summer Holidays

The Mystery Mob have all gone to different places for their holidays. Lee and Rob are in Spain. Gummy and Dwayne are in Italy. Chet and Adi are in India.

Adi I bet Lee and Rob are having a great time in Spain at the All-Stars soccer camp.

Chet   Maybe, but Rob's not very good at football.

Adi   Yeah, he's like Cinderella – he keeps running away from the ball.

Chet   Right! Well, I know Dwayne and Gummy are excited about being in Italy. Dwayne wants to see the Leaning Tower of Pisa.

Adi   Uh-oh! Gummy's in for a big shock. He thinks they've gone to Italy to eat a leaning tower of pizza!

Chet   Shame! Well, at least we're having a fantastic time staying in my Auntie's village here in India.

Adi   Yeah, it's awesome.

Chet's Auntie-ji walks into the room.

Chet   Hey, Auntie-ji, can we go off exploring in the jungle?

Auntie   Yes, but don't go too far, and don't get lost.

Adi   We won't. Er … are there any tigers in the jungle?

Auntie   No. There hasn't been a tiger in our jungle for ages. Poachers killed them all.

Chet   That's terrible. Why did they do that? Were they man-eating tigers?

Auntie   No. The tigers ate deer, they kept away from people. But poachers hunt and kill tigers for their fur and bones.

Chet   Huh. I don't like the sound of them.

Adi   I'm with you, Chet.
It's the poachers who are
the killers – not the tigers.

Chet   I love tigers. They're my
favourite animal. If only we'd
got here sooner. Maybe then
we could have done something
to help save them, Auntie-ji.

Auntie   I don't think you two boys could have done anything to stop the poachers.

Adi   (sighing) I guess not. Come on, Chet. Let's go. At least we can still go exploring in the jungle.

Tiger! Tiger!

Chet and Adi are deep in the jungle.
Chet is swinging on a vine.

Chet   OYOYOYOIYOIYOOOOOO!
I'm Tarzan of the Apes.

Adi   Hey, Chet. Why does Tarzan
wear dark glasses when he goes
into town?

Chet	I don't know.
Adi	Because he doesn't want anyone to recognise him!
Chet	Doh!
Adi	(gulping) Chet, did you hear that?
Chet	Yes, I heard your silly joke.
Adi	No, I mean did you hear that growling noise coming from behind those bushes over there?

Chet	Do you mean that growling noise that sounds just like the growling noise a tiger makes?
Adi	That's it.
Chet	Yes.
Adi	But it can't be a tiger – your Auntie said they were all killed by the poachers.

Chet   Okay. So what animal has
         orange fur with black stripes
         like a tiger ... a long tail like
         a tiger ... a growl like a tiger ...
         and big sharp teeth like a tiger?

Adi   Er ... a tiger? Why?

Chet   'Cos that's the animal I can see
         behind the bush.

Adi   So the poachers didn't kill all the tigers after all!

Chet   (excitedly) Which is good news for the tiger.

Adi   But bad news for us. 'Cos here he comes, and he looks upset!

Chet   But we're not poachers.

Adi   Try telling that to the tiger!

A Pain in the Paw

A huge tiger comes towards Adi and Chet.
They turn to try and run away, but then
Chet stops.

Chet   Hold up, Adi. There's something
         wrong with the tiger.
         He's limping.

Adi   Hey, that gives us a chance.
If the tiger's limping, we may
just be able to outrun him
and get back to the village.
Come on, Chet. I don't fancy
being a tiger's dinner.

Chet   No, he's not growling
'cos he's cross with us.
I think he's growling
'cos he's in pain.

Adi   What do you want me to do about it? Take him to the vet?

Chet   No, but I think we should try to help him.

Adi   How?

Chet   Well, he's holding up his paw. I'm going to see what's wrong with it.

Adi   Chet! You're being stupid. And don't you know that a tiger's favourite food is baked beings?

Chet   Be quiet, Adi. You're scaring him.

Adi   Well, fair's fair, Chet.
He's scaring me.

Chet takes the tiger's paw and looks
at it carefully.

Chet   Ah! I see what's wrong.
The tiger's got a big thorn
in his paw. No wonder he's
in pain.

Adi   Can you take it out?

Chet   I'm going to try. Come here and hold the tiger's paw steady for me.

Adi   All right, but I just hope this big cat doesn't think I'll make a purrfect snack.

Chet   No way. He's heard your jokes so he knows you'll taste a bit funny.

Adi   Ha ha – not! Just get on with it, Chet.

Chet   Right, here goes.

Chet gently takes the thorn out of
the tiger's paw. The tiger sighs with relief.
He licks both their faces.

Adi   Wow! I think he likes us, Chet.

A Tiger's Tale

The tiger lets the boys stroke him
and scratch behind his ears. Adi wants
to tell the tiger his favourite tiger joke.

Chet   I'm not sure telling the tiger
a joke is a good idea, Adi.

Adi   Yes, it is – he'll love it.
Hey, Mr Tiger, what's striped
and bouncy?

The tiger looks at Adi, but he doesn't say anything.

Chet   Go on, then, Adi. What is striped and bouncy?

Adi   A tiger on a trampoline!

Chet   (groaning) That's awful.

The tiger opens its mouth wide and yawns. Then it puts its huge head down on its paws and goes to sleep.

Adi   Huh! I didn't think my joke
was that bad.

Chet   Adi, that joke was so terrible
it was a big cat-astrophe!

Suddenly the boys hear the sound of
a jeep coming along the jungle track.
The tiger wakes up, growls and swishes
its tail angrily from side to side.

Chet   My cat back home swishes
his tail like that when he's mad
at something. So I think
we've got one unhappy
tiger here.

Adi   He's not fed up with us, is he?

Chet   No, but he doesn't seem to like
            the sound of that jeep.

Adi   I wonder why?

The jeep races into the clearing and skids
to a halt. The tiger leaps to its feet
and bounds off into the jungle. It's soon
out of sight. Two men jump down
from the jeep.

Chet   (puzzled) Who are these guys?

Adi   I think we're just about
            to find out.

A Purrfect Ending

The two grim-faced men walk over
to Chet and Adi.

Chet You scared away the tiger.
But there was no need to do that.
We weren't in any danger.
He's our friend.

Adi But I don't think the tiger
wants to be friends with you two.

Man 1   That's right, son. That tiger knows who we are. We've been tracking him.

Chet   Are you game wardens?

The two men laugh nastily.

Adi   These guys don't look like game wardens to me. I think they're …

Chet   Poachers!

Man 2   You got it!

Adi   But poaching is against the law.

Chet   Yeah, that's right. We need to save tigers, not kill them.

The men just sneer at the boys. It's clear they don't care about tigers. Things are not looking good for Chet and Adi – or for the tiger.

Adi   (firmly) We're going to report you guys to the police as soon as we get back to the village.

Man 1   Now that is a really bad idea. We can't let you do that.

Chet   You can't stop us.

Man 2   Oh yes, we can. You two
are going to get so lost
in the jungle that you'll never
come out again!

Adi   (shouting) Help!

Chet   Save your breath, Adi.
No one can hear us out here
in the jungle.

But Chet is wrong. There is a tremendous
roar and the tiger bursts into the clearing.
He's scary! The two poachers back away
from him. The tiger glares at them
and growls.

Adi   Hey, are we glad to see you,
           Tiger!

The tiger prowls over to Adi and Chet.
He stands by them like their own
personal bodyguard.

Chet I'd run for it if I were you.
We can only hold the tiger back
for a second. He's hungry,
and he wants poached poacher
for his tea.

Adi Yeah – there's only one thing
sharper than a tiger's appetite,
and that's his fangs!

The tiger roars and the poachers run for their lives! When they are gone the tiger licks Chet and Adi's faces once more. Then it walks off into the jungle.

Chet   Wow, that tiger is awesome!

Adi   He sure is.

Chet   You know, I'd hate to be those two poachers if the tiger ever catches up with them.

Adi   True – but that tiger's a purrfect pussycat with you and me!

About the author

Roger Hurn has:

- had a hit record in Turkey
- won *The Weakest Link* on TV
- swum with sharks on the Great Barrier Reef.

Now he's a writer, and he hopes you like reading about the Mystery Mob as much as he likes writing about them.

Wild animal quiz

Questions

1 How do you write an essay on an elephant?

2 What do you call an elephant that never washes?

3 Which animal is stronger – a snail or an elephant?

4 Why do bears have fur coats?

5 What kind of tiles can't you stick on walls?

6 What has antlers and sucks blood?

7 What lives in gum trees?

8 Why is it better to be a grasshopper than a cricket?

Answers

1 You get a big ladder and an extra-large pen!
2 A smellyphant!
3 A snail. It carries its house on its back, but an elephant only carries its trunk!
4 Because they look daft in anoraks!
5 Reptiles!
6 A moose-quito!
7 Stick insects!
8 Because grasshoppers can play cricket, but crickets can't play grasshopper!

How did you score?

🖐 If you got all eight wild animal answers correct, then you are a roaring success!

🖐 If you got six wild animal answers correct, then you are a big noise in the jungle!

🖐 If you got fewer than four wild animal answers correct, then you're more of a Tigger than a Tiger!

When I was a kid

Question Did you ever meet a tiger
when you were a kid?

Roger Yes. My dad had a tiger as a pet.

Question Really?

Roger Yes. One day a policeman saw
the tiger sitting next to my dad
in our car.

Question What did the policeman say?

Roger He ordered my dad to take the tiger
to the zoo.

Question Did your dad do that?

Roger No, he took the tiger to the cinema.

Question Why?

Roger Because the tiger wanted to see
a movie – not a bunch of other
animals.

Adi's favourite wild animal joke

What do you get if you cross a tiger with a sheep?

A stripy sweater!

How to survive in the jungle

 Don't be like Tarzan and go chasing after elephants swinging on vines. Elephants don't swing on vines – they live on the ground.

 If your jeep breaks down in the jungle, ask a baboon to help you. He's sure to have a monkey wrench.

 Don't make friends with the chimpanzees – they'll only try to get you involved in monkey business.

 Don't go into the jungle without your hat. If you do, the hot sun will send you bananas.

 Remember, tigers can leap up to 6 metres so always make sure you're standing 7 metres away if you see one.

 Some of the snakes in the jungle can be very friendly – but leave at once if you think a python is getting a crush on you!

 If you cross a river in the jungle, watch out for the crocodiles – they can be very snappy.

 If you leave the jungle by river boat, take care how you get out of the boat when you get back to the town. If your shoes fill up with water, you've probably stepped out the wrong side!

Five fantastic facts about tigers

1   A tiger's tail is almost half as long
    as its entire body. It helps
    the tiger to keep its balance.

2   Stripes help a tiger to camouflage itself
    in the bushes. So, be very careful of bushes
    – they might contain camouflaged tigers!

3   The adult tiger has about 30 large teeth.
    Its canine teeth are razor-sharp and from
    7.5 to 9 centimetres long. I'd really hate
    to be a tiger's dentist!

4   Most tigers have round yellow eyes.
    Tigers can see over six times better
    than humans at night. So going for a stroll
    in the jungle after dark is NOT a great idea!

5   Tigers use their claws to climb trees. If you
    see claw marks on trees in the jungle
    that means you are in a tiger's territory.
    If you see big claw marks on the tree in your
    back garden, stay indoors and phone
    the zoo. It means their tiger has escaped!

Wild animal lingo

Eagle-eyed Eagles have really
good eyesight – like eagle-eyed Gummy
when he spots the last chocolate in the box.

Frog in the throat People say you have this
when you've got a croaky voice. I mean,
not even Gummy gets so hungry that he'd try
and swallow a frog!

Making a beeline Honey bees take the most
direct route they can between two different places
– like Gummy making a beeline for the table
when his mum says his tea is ready.

Playing possum This is when you pretend
to be asleep or even dead. Gummy plays possum
when his mum wants him to help with
the washing up.

Wild-goose chase This means trying to do
something that's impossible. Gummy's on
a wild-goose chase to try and find
the perfect pizza.

Mystery Mob

Mystery Mob Set 1:

Mystery Mob and the Abominable Snowman
Mystery Mob and the Big Match
Mystery Mob and the Circus of Doom
Mystery Mob and the Creepy Castle
Mystery Mob and the Haunted Attic
Mystery Mob and the Hidden Treasure
Mystery Mob and the Magic Bottle
Mystery Mob and the Missing Millions
Mystery Mob and the Monster on the Moor
Mystery Mob and the Mummy's Curse
Mystery Mob and the Time Machine
Mystery Mob and the UFO

Mystery Mob Set 2:

Mystery Mob and the Ghost Town
Mystery Mob and the Bonfire Night Plot
Mystery Mob and the April Fools' Day Joker
Mystery Mob and the Great Pancake Day Race
Mystery Mob and the Scary Santa
Mystery Mob and the Conker Conspiracy
Mystery Mob and the Top Talent Contest
Mystery Mob and the Night in the Waxworks
Mystery Mob and the Runaway Train
Mystery Mob and the Wrong Robot
Mystery Mob and the Day of the Dinosaurs
Mystery Mob and the Man-eating Tiger

RISING ★ STARS

Mystery Mob books are available from most booksellers.

**For mail order information
please call Rising Stars on freephone 0800 091 1602
or visit www.risingstars-uk.com**